POEMS FOR
9
YEAR OLDS

CHOSEN BY

Susie Gibbs

ILLUSTRATED BY

Natacha Ledwidge

MACMILLAN CHILDREN'S BOOKS

Dedicated with love to all my nephews and nieces:
George Henry Cormick, Nicholas John, Mustafa Noah,
Lütfiye, Patrick Charles, Hatice Sara, Ayse Filiz and
Zenda Amy Lily Sunshine.

First published 1999
by Macmillan Children's Books
a division of Macmillan Publishers Ltd
25 Eccleston Place, London SW1W 9NF
Basingstoke and Oxford
www.macmillan.co.uk

Associated companies throughout the world

ISBN 0 330 36964 4
This collection copyright © Susie Gibbs1999
Illustrations copyright © Natacha Ledwidge 1999

The right of Susie Gibbs to be identified as the
author of this book has been asserted by her in accordance
with the Copyright, Designs and Patents Act 1988.

1 3 5 7 9 8 6 4 2

A CIP catalogue record for this book is available from the British Library.

Printed by Mackays of Chatham plc, Chatham, Kent.

Contents

In Praise of Noses

Not exactly ornamental
even when quite straight,
these funny, two-holed things!

But think:
if they faced upwards
they'd blow hats off

when one sneezed
and fill with rain
when it poured.

If sideways,
what objects of derision
snuff-takers would be!

Now all that a sneeze merits
is a 'God bless'.

God bless indeed, sweet nose,
warming, filtering,

humidifying the air as I breathe,
you do a marvellous job!

Prabhu S. Guptara

Weasels

He should have been at school
but instead, he was in bed,
his room more cheerful, brighter,
sheets and pillows whiter
than they'd ever been before.

Comics, bread with crusts cut off,
a jug of homemade lemonade,
Mum's hand so cool against his brow.
Now he had her to himself at last
he'd never want to go to school again.

And all because of little spots,
he raised his vest and thanked them.
Crimson pinpricks on his chest
– some clustered, some quite lonely –
like baby strawberries or beetroot.

Dr Croker joked and felt his muscles.
'Superman! You'll soon be right as rain.'
But his voice from down the stairs
was stern and rather solemn
– and Mummy's sounded scared.

He strained to hear the words,
but they were speaking low. He slipped
out of bed, tiptoed to the door,
pressed his ear against the floor.

'Weasels. He's got weasels, I'm afraid.'
Weasels! He lay in bed and trembled.
Weasels. Furry-grey with pointed teeth.
They must have crept in as he slept,
gnawed and nibbled through the night.
He wondered how much of him was left.

His foot itched. Was it a hidden weasel?
Ankle, knee. Lots of them were there!
He screamed and she came flying.
Her arms were safe as blankets.
He didn't want to stop crying for a while.

John Latham

Coolscorin' Matchwinnin' Celebratin' Striker!

I'm a shirt removin' crowd salutin'
handstandin' happy landin'
rockin' rollin' divin' slidin'
posin' poutin' loud shoutin'
pistol packin' smoke blowin'
flag wavin' kiss throwin'
hipswingin' armwavin'
breakdancin' cool ravin'
shoulder shruggin' team huggin'
hot shootin' rootin' tootin'
somersaultin' fence vaultin'
last minute goal grinnin'
shimmy shootin' shin spinnin'
celebratin' cup winnin' STRIKER!

Paul Cookson

Wings

If I had wings
   I would touch the fingertips of clouds
      and glide on the wind's breath.

If I had wings
   I would taste a chunk of the sun
      as hot as peppered curry.

If I had wings
   I would listen to the clouds of sheep bleat
      that graze on the blue.

If I had wings
   I would breathe deep and sniff
      the scent of raindrops.

If I had wings
   I would gaze at the people
      who cling on the earth's crust.

If I had wings
   I would dream of
      swimming the deserts
         and walking the seas.

Pie Corbett

Jabberwocky

'Twas brillig, and the slithy toves
   Did gyre and gimble in the wabe;
All mimsy were the borogoves,
     And the mome raths outgrabe.

'Beware the Jabberwock, my son!
   The jaws that bite, the claws that catch!
Beware the Jubjub bird, and shun
     The frumious Bandersnatch!'

He took his vorpal sword in hand:
   Long time the manxome foe he sought –
So rested he by the Tumtum tree,
     And stood awhile in thought.

And as in uffish thought he stood,
   The Jabberwock, with eyes of flame,
Came whiffling through the tulgey wood,
     And burbled as it came!

One, two! One, two! And through and through
   The vorpal blade went snicker-snack!
He left it dead, and with its head
     He went galumphing back.

'And hast thou slain the Jabberwock?
    Come to my arms, my beamish boy!
O frabjous day! Callooh! Callay!'
    He chortled in his joy.

'Twas brillig, and the slithy toves
    Did gyre and gimble in the wabe;
All mimsy were the borogoves,
    And the mome raths outgrabe.

Lewis Carroll

Early Start

Where does he
get his skill from;
that body swerve
and fancy footwork?

He's a natural, sir.
Dribbled since
he was a baby.

John C. Desmond

Mary Had a Little Lamb

Mary had a little lamb,
A lobster, and some prunes,
A glass of milk, a piece of pie,
And then some macaroons.

It made the busy waiters grin
To see her order so,
And when they carried Mary out,
Her face was white as snow.

Anon

Father Heard His Children Scream

Father heard his children scream,
So he threw them in the stream,
Saying, as he dropped the third,
'Children should be seen, *not* heard.'

Harry Graham

Just in Case

When it's nearly my birthday
And so that people won't be upset
Or forget,
I always think it's kinder,
Just as a reminder,
To leave notes on plates,
Hinting at dates.

Max Fatchen

This Little Poem

This little poem has five lines
and five words on every line.
I wrote it out five times
between five o'clock and five past nine
using five different pencils every time
and this little poem tells lies.

Ian McMillan

The Wild Yorkshire Pudding

On moors we are hunting
The wild Yorkshire pudding;
The small ones are nippy,
The fat ones are grunting.

They snuggle together
And hide in the heather;
The young ones are tasty,
The old ones like leather.

We jump on and snatch 'em;
They shriek as we catch 'em;
On cords which take twenty
We string and attach 'em.

They dry them in Batley;
They can them in Ilkley.
You will find they are served
Where menus are stately.

Our terriers are scenting
The rock-crevice-skulking
Tremendous with gravy
And wild Yorkshire pudding.

Alan Dixon

The Snake's Warning

A coil of power,
A twist of speed,
Hider in grass,
Content in jungles,
Footless, wingless,
I have powers beasts lack,
Strength birds seek
In clean skies which
Are not my home.
If footsteps approach
Or I hear a twig
Break I alert
At once. My tongue
Means painful death.
Keep your hands off me.

There are men, a few,
With a special gift
To whom I surrender.
I sway to the sound
Of their flutes but I keep
My glance upon them.
They hypnotise me,
Don't ask me how
Or when or why,
If *you* want to be safe,
Keep away, don't try
To tame me with flutes.
If you do, you will die.

Elizabeth Jennings

A Mouthful of Manhattan

Tantalising smells, spicy and strong,
Wrap themselves around us
And reel us in,
Like fish on an aromatic line,
Towards the kerbside kitchens
Of the street vendors' stands.
Queues of crisp, dark-suited men,
Fresh from air-conditioned offices,
Mingle with the garish shorts and shirts
Of the sweaty, suntanned tourists.
All eyes are focused on the feast
Being cooked in the humid New York heat.
Sausages, the size of cucumbers,
Sizzle inside their skins;
Pretzels, the size of dinner plates,
Plaited in salty rings;
Burgers in seeded buns,
Dripping with fried onions.
While the sun squints,
Sending shafts of red-hot spears
Between the stiff, skyscraper silhouettes,
Trucks and taxis and limousines
Tear past, oblivious
To the mouthwatering mountains

Of charcoaled chicken,
Roasted nuts
And sugared doughnuts;
Oblivious, to the star
Of the Manhattan street vendors:
Omar,
'The falafel man'.

With a flourish,
He ladles streams of eggplant sauce
Over fistfuls of salad
And flattened fried falafel,
Stuffed into huge pitta bread pouches,
Which never seem to get smaller,
No matter how much you chew!
Drooling, we attach ourselves
To the end of his queue,
Hypnotised by the tantalising smells,
Spicy and strong,
Which wrapped themselves around us
And drew us along,
To lunch at Omar's,
For a mouthful of Manhattan.

Nisha Doshi (9)

There Was a Young Lad of St Just

There was a young lad of St Just
Who ate apple pie till he bust;
   It wasn't the fru-it
   That caused him to do it,
What finished him off was the crust.

Anon

The Older the Violin the Sweeter the Tune

Me Granny old
Me Granny wise
stories shine like a moon
from inside she eyes.

Me Granny can dance
Me Granny can sing
but she can't play violin.

Yet she always saying,
'Dih older dih violin
de sweeter de tune.'

Me Granny must be wiser
than the man inside the moon.

John Agard

How Do I Love Thee?

How do I love thee? Let me count the ways.
I love thee to the depth and breadth and height
My soul can reach, when feeling out of sight
For the ends of Being and ideal Grace.
I love thee to the level of every day's
Most quiet need, by sun and candle-light.
I love thee freely, as men strive for Right;
I love thee purely, as they turn from Praise.
I love thee with the passion put to use
In my old griefs, and with my childhood's faith.
I love thee with a love I seemed to lose
With my lost saints – I love thee with the breath,
Smiles, tears, of all my life! – and, if God choose,
I shall but love thee better after death.

Elizabeth Barrett Browning

Daisy and Michael

Daisy, Daisy,
Give me your answer do,
I'm half crazy
All for the love of you;
It won't be a stylish marriage,
For I can't afford a carriage –
But you'll look sweet
Upon the seat
Of a bicycle made for two!

Michael, Michael,
This is my answer, dear,
I can't cycle
Always it makes me queer;
If you can't afford a carriage
There will not be a marriage –
For I'll be blowed
If I'll be towed
On a bicycle made for two!

Anon

The Way Through the Woods

They shut the road through the woods
Seventy years ago.
Weather and rain have undone it again,
And now you would never know
There was once a road through the woods
Before they planted the trees.
It is underneath the coppice and heath
And the thin anemones.
Only the keeper sees
That, where the ring-dove broods,
And the badgers roll at ease,
There was once a road through the woods.

Yet, if you enter the woods
Of a summer evening late,
When the night-air cools on the trout-ringed pools
Where the otter whistles his mate,
(They fear not men in the woods,
Because they see so few.)
You will hear the beat of a horse's feet.
And the swish of a skirt in the dew,
Steadily cantering through
The misty solitudes,
As though they perfectly knew
The old lost road through the woods . . .
But there is no road through the woods.

Rudyard Kipling

The Jumblies

They went to sea in a Sieve, they did,
  In a Sieve they went to sea:
In spite of all their friends could say,
On a winter's morn, on a stormy day,
  In a Sieve they went to sea!
And when the Sieve turned round and round,
And every one cried, 'You'll all be drowned!'
They called aloud, 'Our Sieve ain't big,
But we don't care a button! we don't care a fig!
  In a Sieve we'll go to sea!'
    Far and few, far and few,
      Are the lands where the Jumblies live;
     Their heads are green, and their hands are blue,
      And they went to sea in a Sieve.

They sailed away in a Sieve, they did,
  In a Sieve they sailed so fast,
With only a beautiful pea-green veil
Tied with a riband by way of a sail,
  To a small tobacco-pipe mast;
And every one said, who saw them go,
'O won't they be soon upset, you know!
For the sky is dark, and the voyage is long,
And happen what may, it's extremely wrong
  In a Sieve to sail so fast!'
    Far and few, far and few,
      Are the lands where the Jumblies live;
     Their heads are green, and their hands are blue,
      And they went to sea in a Sieve.

The water it soon came in, it did,
   The water it soon came in;
So to keep them dry, they wrapped their feet
In a pinky paper all folded neat,
     And they fastened it down with a pin.
And they passed the night in a crockery-jar,
And each of them said, 'How wise we are!
Though the sky be dark, and the voyage be long,
Yet we never can think we were rash or wrong,
   While round in our Sieve we spin!'
     Far and few, far and few,
        Are the lands where the Jumblies live;
      Their heads are green, and their hands are blue,
       And they went to sea in a Sieve.

And all night long they sailed away;
   And when the sun went down,
They whistled and warbled a moony song
To the echoing sound of a coppery gong,
   In the shade of the mountains brown.
'O Timballo! How happy we are,
When we live in a sieve and a crockery-jar,
And all night long in the moonlight pale,
We sail away with a pea-green sail,
   In the shade of the mountains brown!'
     Far and few, far and few,
        Are the lands where the Jumblies live;
      Their heads are green, and their hands are blue,
       And they went to sea in a Sieve.

They sailed to the Western Sea, they did,
   To a land all covered with trees,
And they bought an Owl, and a useful Cart,
And a pound of Rice, and a Cranberry Tart,
   And a hive of silvery Bees.
And they bought a Pig, and some green Jack-daws,
And a lovely Monkey with lollipop paws,
And forty bottles of Ring-Bo-Ree,
   And no end of Stilton Cheese.
     Far and few, far and few,
        Are the lands where the Jumblies live;
      Their heads are green, and their hands are blue,
        And they went to sea in a Sieve.

And in twenty years they all came back,
   In twenty years or more,
And every one said, 'How they've grown!
For they've been to the Lakes, and the Torrible Zone,
   And the hills of the Chankly Bore;
And they drank their health, and gave them a feast
Of dumplings made of beautiful yeast;
And every one said, 'If we only live,
We too will go to sea in a Sieve, –
   To the hills of the Chankley Bore!'
     Far and few, far and few,
        Are the lands where the Jumblies live;
      Their heads are green, and their hands are blue,
        And they went to sea in a Sieve.

Edward Lear

What Have We Got
in the House?

I think I know what we've got in the house.
When it moves, it makes more mess than a mouse.
So, what do you think we've got in the house?

We found egg-shell down
By the washing machine
And four claw-prints
In the margarine.

I think I know what we've got in the house.
When it moves, it makes more mess than a mouse,
Or a rat, or a roach, or a louse.
So, what do you think we've got in the house?

The sides of the bath
Are greenish-tinged
And the spare toothbrush
Has had its bristles singed.

I think I know what we've got in the house.
When it moves, it makes more mess than a mouse.
Or a rat, or a roach, or a louse,
Or a gerbil, or an oyster, or a grouse.
So, what do you think we've got in the house?

We've never had a fire
But I often cough.
Then the smoke alarm
In the hall goes off.

I think I know what we've got in the house.
When it moves, it makes more mess than a mouse.
Or a rat, or a roach, or a louse,
Or a gerbil, or an oyster, or a grouse,
Or a duck-billed platypus together with its spouse.
So, what do you think we've got in the house?

There are long scratch-marks
Just like from claws
Around the handles
Of all the doors.

I think I know what we've got in the house.
Don't you?

Nick Toczek

Rant About Pants

Some people call them knickers
My Granny calls them drawers
Hers used to keep the cold out
Now they're used for cleaning floors

Florists call them bloomers
And lawyers call them briefs
While undertakers solemnly say
A pair of underneaths

Fire fighters call them hosiery
Americans call them panties
Which are the nasty nylon kind
You get from distant aunties

Small people call them long johns
Tall people call them shorts
There's even combinations
Designed to fit all sorts

Lurking beneath a Scotsman's kilt
You're unlikely to find any
Which makes it nice and easy
When he wants to spend a penny

There are bikinis, teeny-weenies
Trunks with no frills or fuss
You should always wear a fresh pair
In case you're knocked down by a bus

There are hundreds of words for underwear
But I always call mine pants
They're white and clean and seldom seen
And they rhyme so well with ants

Lindsay MacRae

Fantasia

I dream
of
giving birth
to
a child
who will ask,
'Mother,
what was war?'

Eve Merriam

I Can't Say That

Dear Auntie Beryl,
Thanks for the Christmas present.
It was lovely –
except twenty-four-piece puzzles are much too easy
for my age.
Mum's put it away for the baby.
I can't say that.

Dear Pen Pal,
Thanks for your letter.
You've got very nice handwriting.
Your holiday in the Bahamas sounded smashing.
We went to Weston this year
and it rained every single minute
except the afternoon we were going home.
I can't say that.

Dear Santa,
There's a whole string of presents
I'd really like to have
But why were the only ones I got last year
the little ones?
I can't say that.

Dear Teacher,
I think it's a very good idea
to practise writing letters,
but I already know
where to put the address and the date
and the postcode and the 'Yours sincerely',
and the 'With love from' –
it's the bit in between I find difficult.
I can't say that.

Brian Morse

Having My Ears Boxed

I am waiting in the corridor
To have my ears boxed.
I am nervous, for Mr O'Hanlon
Is a beast of his word.

For the last twenty minutes
I have let my imagination
Run away with itself.
But I am too scared to follow.

Will he use that Swiss Army knife
To slice through cleanly? Bite them off?
Tear carefully along perforated lines?
Tug sharply like loose Elastoplasts?

Acknowledging the crowd's roar
Will he hold my head aloft
As if it were the FA Cup
And pull the handles? Aagghhrr . . .

And then the box. Cardboard?
Old cigar-box possibly? Or a pair?
Separate coffins of polished pine.
Left and Right. 'Gone to a better place.'

Impatient now, I want to get it
Over with. Roll on four o'clock.
When, hands over where-my-ears-used-to-be
I run the gauntlet of jeering kids.

At six, mother arrives home weary
After a hard day at the breadcrumb factory.
I give her the box. She opens it
And screams something. I say:

'Pardon?'

Roger McGough

Getting There

Call for a taxi Maxie,
Or phone for a mini-cab;
Don't worry about the meter,
I'll gladly pick up the tab.

Ignore the doorman Norman,
The cabbies are all on strike;
It's got to be Shanks's Pony,
Or getting on your bike.

Jump on the ferry Jerry,
It sails on the morning tide;
All day the bars will stay open
On the port (and the sherry) side.

Leap on your cycle Michael,
And zoom away fast, then display
The proper hand-signal for Norman,
Should you happen to meet on the way.

On to your scooter Pooter,
As pompous as pompous can be;
The tin-tacks we've spread out will puncture
Your tyres and your vanity.

Into your Morris Doris;
I wish I'd been given the chance
To join you; we'd park and together
Alight for a quick Morris dance.

Drive the jallopy Poppy;
It's ancient but none of us care
How bumpy and lengthy the journey
As long as we get safely there.

Vernon Scannell

She Dwelt Among the Untrodden Ways

She dwelt among the untrodden ways
   Beside the springs of Dove,
A maid whom there were none to praise
   And very few to love:

A violet by a mossy stone
   Half hidden from the eye!
Fair as a star, when only one
   Is shining in the sky.

She lived unknown, and few could know
   When Lucy ceased to be;
But she is in her grave, and, oh,
   The difference to me!

William Wordsworth

Relatives

*(A Poem To Say Fast
When You Want To Show Off)*

My father's and mother's sisters and brothers
Are called my uncles and aunts
(Except when they're called *ma tante* and *mon oncle*
Which happens if they're in France.)
Now the daughters and sons of my uncles and aunts
Are my cousins. (Confusion increases –
Since if you're my mother or if you're my Dad,
Then those cousins are nephews and nieces.)

Jeff Moss

The Alien Wedding

When the aliens got married,
The bride was dressed in zeet;
And with a flumzel in her groyt,
She really looked a treat.

The groom was onggy spoodle,
He felt a little quenz;
The best man told him not to cronk
In front of all their friends.

The bride's ensloshid father
Had slupped down too much glorter;
He grobbled up the aisle alone,
Then flomped back for his daughter.

The lushen bridesmaids followed
With such wigantic walks;
Their optikacious oggers
Were sparkling on their stalks.

The bride and groom entroathed their splice,
They swapped a little squip;
Then he splodged her on the kisser,
And she flimped him on the blip.

And after the wedding breakfast,
The stroadling and the laughter,
The loving pair took off to Mars,
And splayed winkerly ever after.

Mike Jubb

From a Railway Carriage

Faster than fairies, faster than witches,
Bridges and houses, hedges and ditches;
And charging along like troops in a battle,
All through the meadows the horses and cattle;
All of the sights of the hill and the plain
Fly as thick as driving rain;
And ever again, in the wink of an eye,
Painted stations whistle by.

Here is a child who clambers and scrambles,
All by himself and gathering brambles;
Here is a tramp who stands and gazes;
And there is the green for stringing the daises!
Here is a cart run away in the road
Lumping along with man and load;
And here is a mill, and there is a river:
Each a glimpse and gone for ever!

R.L. Stevenson

I Lost My Voice

Did I lose my voice
  on an InterCity train?
Or is it soaking through the soil
  with the pouring rain?

I lost my voice,
  and I don't know where to look,
Perhaps I pressed it flat
  between the pages of a book?

Did I lose my voice
  on a busy street corner?
Maybe it's drowning
  in a bottle of Kia-Ora,

I lost my voice,
  and I'm short on words,
Maybe I forgot myself
  and fed it to the birds?

Did I lose my voice
  at a supermarket checkout?
Perhaps it slipped from lips
  just before the shout?

I lost my voice,
  I've almost given up the search,
Maybe someone's found it
  on a pew in church?

I lost my voice
  and I want it back,
Is it lurking in the pocket
  of my plastic mack?

Could it be that butterfly,
  buffeting the breeze?
Perhaps the split second
  just before a sneeze?

I lost my voice
  And I want it ba

Simon Pitt

Baby Rap!

Adults go gooey with a baby on their lap,
it's the cootchy-coo, cuddly-poo baby rap.

Woopsy, poopsy, honey bun,
sweetie, tweetie, sugar plum,
snuggums, diddums, cutesie tootsie,
bunnikins, honeykins, footsie wootsie.

Out on the street adults push their buggies,
desperate for coos and lots of huggies.
When baby cries; time to change that nap,
parents smile for it's their time to rap!

Woopsy, poopsy, honey bun,
sweetie, tweetie, sugar plum,
snuggums, diddums, cutesie tootsie,
bunnikins, honeykins, footsie wootsie.

Adults enjoy being a patter chatterbox
with 'precious, izzums, bless your cotton socks.'
So when babies cry, 'daddeeee, mummeeee,'
all adults do is shove in a dummy!

Woopsy, poopsy, honey bun,
sweetie, tweetie, sugar plum,
snuggums, diddums, cutesie tootsie,
bunnikins, honeykins, footsie wootsie.

Babies must wonder what's happening here,
all this cooey talk dribbling in their ear.
Those adults so noisy and full of prattle
perhaps their mouths should be stuffed with
    a RATTLE!

Woopsy, poopsy, honey bun,
sweetie, tweetie, sugar plum,
snuggums, diddums, cutesie tootsie,
bunnikins, honeykins, footsie wootsie.

Adults go gooey with a baby on their lap,
it's the cootchy-coo, cuddly-poo baby rap!

Ian Souter

The Invisible Man's
Invisible Dog

My invisible dog is not much fun.
I don't know if he's glad or glum.
I don't know if, when I pat his head,
I'm really patting his bum instead.

Brian Patten

Teacher's Pet

Teacher's pet isn't Billy
or Darren or Sharon or Lee,
Teacher's pet isn't Sally
or Vicky or Nicky or me,
Teacher's hunting for her pet,
She's crawling around on all fours,
Teacher's pet is a big black spider
And she keeps it in her drawers.

Roger Stevens

Hlep

Something has gone wrog in the garden.
There are doffadils blooming in the nose-beds,
And all over the griss dandeloons
Wave their ridigulous powdered wigs.

Under the wipping willop, in the pond
Where the whiter-lollies flute,
I see goldfinches swamming
And the toepaddles changing into fargs.

The griss itself is an unusual shade of groon
And the gote has come loose from its honges.
It's all extrepely worlying!
Helg me, some baddy! Heap me!

And it's not unly in the ganden.
These trumbles have fellowed me indares.
The toble has grown an extra log
And the Tally won't get Baby-See-Too.

Even my trusty Tygerwriter
Is producing the most peaqueueliar worms.
Helg me Sam Biddy. Kelp me!
Helg! HOLP! HELLO!!

Gerard Benson

The Car Trip

Mum says:
'Right, you two,
this is a very long car journey.
I want you two to be good.
I'm driving and I can't drive properly
if you two are going mad in the back.
Do you understand?'

So we say,
OK, Mum, OK. Don't worry,
and off we go.

And we start The Moaning:
Can I have a drink?
I want some crisps.
Can I open my window?
He's got my book.
Get off me.
Ow, that's my ear!

And Mum tries to be exciting:
'Look out the window
there's a lamp-post.'

And we go on with The Moaning:
Can I have a sweet?
He's sitting on me.
Are we nearly there?
Don't scratch.

You never tell him off.
Now he's biting his nails.
I want a drink. I want a drink.

And Mum tries to be exciting again:
'Look out the window
there's a tree.'

And we go on:
My hands are sticky.
He's playing with the doorhandle now.
I feel sick.
Your nose is all runny.
Don't pull my hair.
He's punching me, Mum,
That's really dangerous, you know.
Mum, he's spitting.

And Mum says:
'Right I'm stopping the car.
I AM STOPPING THE CAR.'

She stops the car.

'Now, if you two don't stop it
I'm going to put you out of the car
and leave you by the side of the road.'

He started it.
I didn't. He started it.

'I don't care who started it
I can't drive properly
if you two go mad in the back.
Do you understand?'

And we say:
OK Mum, OK, don't worry.

Can I have a drink?

Michael Rosen

A Cornish Charm

From Ghosties and Ghoulies
And long-leggity Beasties,
And all things that go BUMP
In the night –
Good Lord, deliver us!

Anon

I am on the Kids' Side

I am on the kids' side
in the war against adults.
I don't want to stand still.
I don't want to sit still.
I don't want to be quiet.
I believe that strangers
are for staring at,
bags are for looking into,
paper is for scribbling on.
I want to know Why.
I want to know How.
I wonder What If.
I am on the kids' side
in the war against tedium.
I'm for going home
when stores get packed.
I'm for sleeping in
when parties get dull.
I'm for kicking stones
when conversation sags.
I'm for making noises.
I'm for playing jokes –
especially in life's
more Serious Bits.
I am on the kids' side.
See my sneaky grin,
watch me dance, see me run.
Spit on the carpet, rub it in,

pick my nose in public,
play rock stars in the mirror.

I am on the kids' side.
I want to know why we're not moving.
I'm fed up. I want to go out.
What's that? Can I have one?
It isn't fair. Who's that man?
It wasn't me, I was pushed.
When are we going to go?
I am on the kids' side
putting fun back into words.
Ink pink pen and ink
you go out because you stink.
Stephen Turner is a burner,
urner, murner, purner.
Stephen, weven, peven,
reven, teven, Turnip Top.
I am on the kids' side
in the war against apathy.
Mum, I want to do something.
It must be my turn next.
When can we go out?
I am on the kids' side
and when I grow up,
I want to be a boy.

Steve Turner

Tony O

Over the bleak and barren snow
A voice there came a-calling;
'Where are you going to, Tony O!
Where are you going this morning?'

'I am going where there are rivers of wine,
The mountains bread and honey;
There Kings and Queens do mind the swine,
And the poor have all the money.'

Anon

King Foo Foo

King Foo Foo sat upon his throne
Dressed in his royal closes,
While all around his courtiers stood
With clothes-pegs on their noses.

'This action strange,' King Foo Foo said,
'My mind quite discomposes,
Though vulgar curiosity
A good king never shoses.'

But to the court it was as clear
As poetry or prose is:
King Foo Foo had not had a bath
Since goodness only knoses.

Till one fine day the Fire Brigade
Rehearsing with their hoses
(To Handel's 'Water Music' played
With many puffs and bloses)

Quite failed the water to control
In all its ebbs and floses
And simply drenched the King with sev-
Eral thousand gallon doses.

At this each wight (though impolite)
A mighty grin exposes.
'At last,' the King said, 'now I see
That all my court morose is!

'A debt to keep his courtiers glad
A monarch surely oweses,
And deep within my royal breast
A sporting heart reposes.'

So now each night its water bright
The Fire Brigade disposes
Over a King who smiles as sweet
As all the royal roses.

Charles Causley

Whale

Wouldn't you like to be a whale
And sail serenely by –
An eighty-foot whale from the tip of your tail
And a tiny, briny eye?
Wouldn't you like to wallow
Where nobody says 'Come out!'?
Wouldn't you *love* to swallow
And blow all the brine about?
Wouldn't you like to be always clean
But never to have to wash, I mean,
And wouldn't you love to spout –
    O yes, just think –
A feather of spray as you sail away,
And rise and sink and rise and sink,
And blow all the brine about?

Geoffrey Dearmer

Lauren

You're a new daisy
that's come up at night,
your skin is
a silk cover rubbed
against my hand.

You're a moon
drifting through frozen air,
the lady who helps me
when I'm hurt. You are
cream just whipped.

You're a red lipped flower,
the bit of butter
melting on my potato,
you're the hot water in my
bath, rushing around me.

You are god talking
quietly to horses,
a rainbow in the sky.
You're the moment
I get my sums right.

Barry Turrell (9)

FA Rules OK

Life isn't easy in our house
My dad's a referee
He's always right, never wrong
And he knows all the rules.

Everyday he comes home
Shiny black shirt
Shiny black shorts
Shiny red face
Shiny silver whistle.

He races around the house
Checking the nets on the curtains
The height of the crossbars over the doors.

He doesn't like it
When the budgie talks back to him
He gets mad when the dog
Dribbles down his leg
And he booked the cat for spitting.

If we don't wash our hands before tea
That's it – a warning.
Leaving our greens – yellow card.
Giving them to the dog – red card.

Being sent off in your own house
Is no fun.
It's a long lonely walk upstairs
For that early bath
Early bed, no telly
And no extra time.

Yes, life isn't easy in our house
Dad's always right
And he knows all the rules.

Paul Cookson and David Harmer

Lines on Montezuma

Mexican legend by a Passman

Montezuma
Met a puma
Coming through the rye:
Montezuma made the puma
Into apple pie.

Invitation
To the nation
Everyone to come.
Montezuma
And the puma
Give a kettle-drum.

Acceptation
Of the nation
One and all invited.
Montezuma
And the puma
Equally delighted.

Preparation,
Ostentation,
Dresses rich prepared:
Feathers – jewels –
Work in crewels –
No expenses spared.

Congregation
Of the nation
Round the palace wall.
Awful rumour
That the puma
Won't be served to all.

Deputation
From the nation,
Audience they gain.
'What's this rumour?
Montezuma,
If you please, explain.'

Montezuma
(Playful humour
very well sustained)
Answers: 'Piedish
As it's my dish,
Is for me retained.'

Exclamation!
Indignation!
Feeling running high.
Montezuma
Joins the puma
In the apple pie.

D.F. Alderson

All Right, Mum?

I do like your dress, Mum,
it's trendy, and it's cool,
but I'd wear jeans, if I were you,
to meet me from school.

Can you come in Dad's car?
It's not that yours is bad,
but the stickers in the windows
are a bit sad.

I love the way you've done your hair,
but I should wear a scarf.
No, I don't think it's funny
but my friends might laugh.

Your make-up rather suits you.
You know I'm really glad
my best friend told me yesterday
that I look like my dad.

Of course I'm really proud of you.
I'm not at all ashamed,
and if they ask 'Whose mother's that?'
I can't be blamed.

Celia Warren

What No Snow?

Why doesn't it snow?
It's winter, isn't it?
Then it's supposed to snow.
How else can you make snowmen,
Or fight each other with snowballs,
And slide down hills on sledges?

It's not fair, is it?
Soon it will be summer,
Then it'll just rain and rain for months.
Can't anyone tell me,
WHY DOESN'T IT SNOW?

Bill Boyle

Oh, Ozzie!

'Polar bear in the garden!' yelled Ozzie,
And we all rushed out to see,
But of course it wasn't a bear at all –
Just a marmalade cat who'd jumped over the wall.
Oh, Ozzie!

'Mountain lion in the garden!' yelled Ozzie,
And we all rushed out to see,
But of course it wasn't a lion with a roar –
Just the scruffy black dog who'd dug in from
    next door.
Oh, Ozzie!

'Kangaroo in the garden!' yelled Ozzie,
And we all stayed in and smiled,
And of course it wasn't a kangaroo –
But a man-eating tiger escaped from the zoo.
Poor Ozzie.

Richard Edwards

My Sister's Getting Married

My sister's getting married
and it's awful news.
My sister wants a page boy
and it's me she's going to choose!
She's going to buy a satin suit
with frills and lacy stuff,
  a soppy little jacket,
    with soppy little cuffs.

I'm gonna be a page boy!
Please don't tell my mates!
Don't tell 'em where the church is,
Don't tell 'em wedding dates.
  Oh please,
    Oh please don't tell them!

I wish it wasn't true
  My sister's 27
  and I am 42!

Peter Dixon

I'm Nobody

I'm Nobody! Who are you?
Are you – Nobody – too?
Then there's a pair of us! Don't tell!
They'd banish us – you know!

How dreary – to be – Somebody!
How public – like a Frog –
To tell your name – the livelong day –
To an admiring bog!

Emily Dickinson

Henry My Son

'Where have you been all the day,
Henry my son?
Where have you been all the day,
My handsome one?'

'In the woods, dear Mother.
In the woods, dear Mother.
Oh, Mother, be quick
I'm going to be sick
And lay me down to die.'

'Oh, what did you do in the woods,
Henry my boy?
What did you do in the woods,
My pride and joy?'

'Ate, dear Mother.
Ate, dear Mother.
Oh, Mother, be quick
I'm going to be sick
And lay me down to die.'

'Oh, what did you eat in the woods,
Henry my son?
What did you eat in the woods,
My handsome one?'

'Eels, dear Mother.
Eels, dear Mother.
Oh, Mother, be quick
I'm going to be sick
And lay me down to die.'

'Oh, what colour was them eels,
Henry my boy?
What colour was them eels,
My pride and joy?'

'Green and yeller!
Green and yeller!
Oh, Mother, be quick
I'm going to be sick
And lay me down to die.'

'Them eels was snakes
Henry my son.
Them eels was snakes,
My handsome one.'

'Yerr-uck! dear Mother.
Yerr-uck! dear Mother.
Oh, Mother, be quick
I'm going to be sick
And lay me down to die.'

'Oh, what colour flowers would you like,
Henry my son?
What colour flowers would you like,
My handsome one?'

'Green and yeller.
Green and yeller.
Oh, Mother, be quick
I'm going to be sick
And lay me down to die.'

Anon

Class Discussion

'In the class discussion Jane you hardly said a word.
We all aired our opinions but from you we rarely
   heard.
You sat and stared in silence surrounded by the
   chatter,
Now tell me Jane, and please be plain,
Is there anything the matter?'

Jane looked up and then she spoke,
Her voice was clear and low:
There are many people in this world
Who are rather quiet you know!'

Gervase Phinn

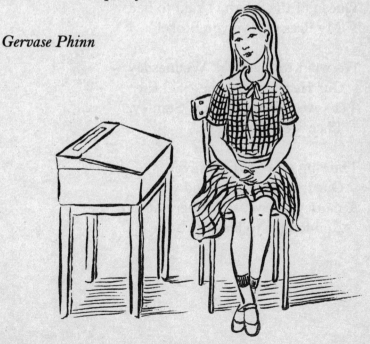

A Perfect Match

We met in Nottingham Forest,
    My sweet Airdrie and I.
She smiled and said, 'Alloa!' to me –
    Oh, never say goodbye!

I asked her, 'Is your Motherwell?'
    And she replied, 'I fear
She's got the Academicals
    From drinking too much beer.'

We sat down on a Meadowbank
    And of my love I spoke.
'Queen of the South,' I said to her,
    'My fires of love you Stoke!'

We went to Sheffield, Wednesday.
    Our Hearts were one. Said she:
'Let's wed in Accrington, Stanley,
    Then we'll United be.'

The ring was Stirling silver,
    Our friends, Forfar and wide,
A motley Crewe, all gathered there
    And fought to kiss the bride.

The best man had an awful lisp.
  'Come Raith your glatheth up,'
He said, and each man raised on high
  His Coca-Cola cup.

The honeymoon was spent abroad:
  We flew out east by Ayr,
And found the far-off Orient
  Partick-ularly fair.

We're home, in our own Villa now,
  (The Walsall painted grey)
And on our Chesterfield we sit
  And watch Match of the Day.

Pam Gidney

Daughter of the Sea

bog seeper
moss creeper
growing restless
getting steeper

trickle husher
swish and rusher
stone leaper
splash and gusher

foam flicker
mirror slicker
pebble pusher
boulder kicker

still pool
don't be fooled
shadow tricker
keeping cool

leap lunger
crash plunger
free fall
with thunder under

idle winder
youth behind her
little wonder
daily grinder

garbage binner
dump it in her
never mind her
dog's dinner

plastic bagger
old lagger
oil skinner
wharf nagger

cargo porter
weary water
tide dragger
long-lost daughter

of the sea
the sea the sea
has caught her
up in its arms and set her free

Philip Gross

Little Lisa

Little Lisa likes to lick
lots and loads of lovely lollies
lime and lychees, melon, lemon,
lychees, lime and lemon, melon,
melon, lemon, lime and lychees,
lemon, melon, lychees, lime.

Licking lollies little Lisa
liked to lick Molly's lollies.
Licking lollies little Lisa
liked to lick Polly's lollies.
Licking lollies little Lisa
liked to lick Holly's lollies.
Molly's lollies, Polly's lollies,
Holly's lollies, jolly lollies
lots and loads and loads and lots
and lots and loads and loads and lots
and lots of lovely jolly lollies
Little Lisa liked to lick.

Little Lisa liked to lick
lots of lovely jolly lollies
nicked the licks from Molly's lollies
licked the nicks from Polly's lollies
quickly licked Holly's lollies
slickly licked lots of lollies
lemon lollies
melon lollies
lychee lollies
lime lollies
lots and lots of lovely lollies
Little Lisa liked to lick.

David Harmer

Conkers

Autumn treasures
from the horsechestnut tree

Lying roly poly
among their split green casings

Shiny and hard
like pops of polished mahogany

An English schoolboy
picking them up –

The same compulsive
fickle avidity –

As I picked up
orange-coloured cockles

Way back then
from a tropical childhood tree

Hand about to close in . . .
then spotting another even better

Now, waiting on our bus
we grown-ups watch him

Not knowing how or why
we've lost our instinct

For gathering
the magic shed of trees

Though in partyful mood
in wineful spirits

We dance around crying,
'give me back my conker.'

Grace Nichols

Good Riddance But Now What?

Come children, gather round my knee;
Something is about to be.

Tonight's December thirty-first,
Something is about to burst.

The clock is crouching, dark and small,
Like a time bomb in the hall.

Hark! It's midnight, children dear.
Duck! Here comes another year.

Ogden Nash

Perfect Paula

Paula is tidy
Paula is good
Paula does everything
nice girls should.

All of the teachers
think Paula is sweet.
But all of our class
know that Paula's a creep.

Lindsay MacRae

On Killing a Tree

It takes much time to kill a tree,
Not a simple jab of the knife
Will do it. It has grown
Slowly consuming the earth,
Rising out of it, feeding
Upon its crust, absorbing
Years of sunlight, air, water,
And out of its leprous hide
Sprouting leaves.

So hack and chop
But this alone won't do it.
Not so much pain will do it.
The bleeding bark will heal
And from close to the ground
Will rise curled green twigs,
Miniature boughs
Which if unchecked will expand again
To former size.

No,
The root is to be pulled out —
Out of the anchoring earth;
It is to be roped, tied,
And pulled out — snapped out
Or pulled out entirely,
Out from the earth-cave,
And the strength of the tree exposed,
The source, white and wet,
The most sensitive, hidden
For years inside the earth.

Then the matter
Of scorching and choking
In sun and air,
Browning, hardening,
Twisting, withering,

And then it is done.

Gieve Patel

Okay, Brown Girl, Okay

*For Josie, 9 years old, who wrote to me saying . . . 'boys called me
names because of my colour. I felt very upset . . . My brother and
sister are English. I wish I was, then I won't be picked on . . .
How do you like being brown?'*

Josie, Josie, I am okay
being brown. I remember,
every day dusk and dawn get born
from the loving of night and light
who work together, like married.
   And they would like to say to you:
   Be at school on and on, brown Josie
   like thousands and thousands and thousands
   of children, who are brown and white
   and black and pale-lemon colour.
   All the time, brown girl Josie is okay.

Josie, Josie, I am okay
being brown. I remember,
every minute sun in the sky
and ground of the earth work together
like married.
   And they would like to say to you:
   Ride on up a going escalator
   like thousands and thousands and thousands
   of people, who are brown and white
   and black and pale-lemon colour.
   All the time, brown girl Josie is okay.

Josie, Josie, I am okay
being brown. I remember,
all the time bright-sky and brown-earth
work together, like married
making forests and food and flowers and rain.
  And they would like to say to you:
  Grow and grow brightly, brown girl.
  Write and read and play and work.
  Ride bus or train or boat or aeroplane
  like thousands and thousands and thousands
  of people, who are brown and white
  and black and pale-lemon colour.
  All the time, brown girl Josie is okay.

James Berry

On Tuesdays I Polish My Uncle

I went to play in the park.
I didn't get home until dark.
But when I got back I had ants in my pants
And my father was feeding the shark.

I went to play in the park,
I didn't get home until dark.
And when I got back I had ants in my pants
And dirt in my shirt, and glue in my shoe,
And my father was tickling the shark.

I went to sleep in the park.
The shark was starting to bark.
And when I woke up I had ants in my pants,
Dirt in my shirt, glue in my shoe,
And my beans in my jeans and a bee on my knee,
And the shark was tickling my father.

My father went off to the park.
I stayed home and read to the shark.
And when he got back he had ants in his pants,
Dirt in his shirt, glue in his shoe,
Beans in his jeans, a bee on his knee,
Beer in his ear and a bear in his hair,
So we put him outside in the ark.

I started the ark in the dark.
My father was parking the shark.
And when we got home we had ants in our pants,
Dirt in our shirt, glue in our shoe,
Beans in our jeans, a bee on our knee,
Beer in our ear and a bear in our hair,
A stinger in our finger, a stain in our brain,
And our belly-buttons shone in the dark.

So my dad he got snarky and barked at the shark
Who was parking the ark on the mark in the dark.
And when they got back they had ants in their
    pants,
Dirt in their shirt, glue in their shoe,
Beans in their jeans, a bee on their knee,
Beer in their ear and a bear in their hair,
A stinger in each finger, a stain in the brain,
A small polka-dot burp, with headache tablets,
And a ship on the lip and a horse, of course,
So we all took a bath in the same tub and went to
    bed early.

Dennis Lee

Here is the Feather Warcast

In the South it will be a dowdy clay
with some shattered scours.
Further North there'll be some hoe and snail
with whales to the guest.
In the East the roaring pain
will give way to some psalmy bun.

Trevor Millum

The Tunneller

    At number 42
there's a hawthorn perimeter hedge
and the front gate is topped
with strands of barbed wire.
The mad Major lives there,
a septuagenarian ex-soldier
with military moustache
and a broom-handle-straight back.

    On a mission,
in the last War, he parachuted into Germany,
was captured, and then held
in a prison camp: Stalag number 39.
He tunnelled out, escaped to England.
His true story is printed in a book
I found at the library:
Spies of the Second World War.

    Yesterday,
at dusk, I hid in his long back garden
and spied on the Major
as he passed the old air-raid shelter
and marched into his garden shed.
He was dressed in black –
trousers, sweater, and woolly Balaclava.
Dirt streaks disguised his face.

    I sneaked up
and through the cobwebby window
watched as the Major removed floorboards,
then lowered himself into a hole
and . . . disappeared!
He was tunnelling again,
digging beneath his back garden,
tunnelling towards the perimeter hedge.

    An hour later
he emerged furtively from the shed
lugging a heavy sack
and I saw him scatter damp soil
between his rhubarb and cauliflowers.
Night after night he's at it,
secretly tunnelling his way to freedom,
trying to escape from Stalag number 42.

Wes Magee

Respire, Aspire, Suspire

There was a young girl in the choir
Whose voice arose higher and higher,
   Till one Sunday night
   It rose quite out of sight,
And they found it next day on the spire.

Anon

Left or Right?

When we all went for a picnic
Mum drove the car
and Dad was navigator.

'Are you sure
you can read the map?'
Mum asked.
'Of course I can.'
Dad said.

We got out into the country.
'Right.'
said Dad.
'At the next junction
turn left. Right?'
So Mum turned right.

'Look, I said left.'
'You said right.'
'Well, get us back then.'
'OK.'

Dad folded the map.
'Now,'
he said
'Turn left, then right. Right?'
'Turn right.'
'No. Left.'

'Left?'
'That's right.'
'But you said left, not right.'
'Right. Left.'
Mum stopped the car.
Her face was traffic light red.
'We're going home.'
she said.
'But Mum . . . '
we all said.
She narrowed her eyes.
'Look, I'm quite happy
to leave you all here.
So be quiet or you'll be
left. Right?'
'Right.'
We said.

We had our picnic
in the garden.
Dad said
'We could try again tomorrow.'
Mum raised her fists.
'Which do you want?'
she said.
'Left or right?'

Robin Mellor

Escape Route

When our teacher came to school today
he looked bright and happy, not old and grey,
not the usual bear whose head was sore,
and we hadn't seen him like this before.
He parked his car in our headteacher's space,
you should have seen the look on her face
as she swept like a hurricane into our room,
and it brightened up our Monday gloom.
But instead of looking a picture of worry
or smiling nervously and saying sorry
he'd go out and shift it straightaway,
our teacher told her that from today
she could stay and teach his class,
and the look on her face was like frosted glass.
He ripped up test papers in front of her eyes,
then jumped up and down, and to our surprise
planted a slobbery kiss on her cheek,
and just for a moment she couldn't speak,
till he told us how on Saturday night
his lottery numbers had all been right.

Then a noise from outside made us look round
as a helicopter landed in our school grounds,
and our teacher said, 'It's my taxi at last,
this school, all of you, are now in my past.'
Then while we watched, the big blades whirred
and he left for the sky as free as a bird.

And his car is still parked in our headteacher's space.
You should have seen the look on her face!

Brian Moses

Sir Smashum Uppe

Good afternoon, Sir Smashum Uppe!
We're having tea: do take a cup!
Sugar and milk? Now let me see –
Two lumps, I think? . . . Good gracious me!
The silly thing slipped off your knee!
Pray don't apologise, old chap:
A very trivial mishap!
So clumsy of you? How absurd!
My dear Sir Smashum, not a word!
Now do sit down and have another,
And tell us all about your brother –
You know, the one who broke his head.
Is the poor fellow still in bed?
A chair – allow me, sir! . . . Great Scott!
That *was* a nasty smash! Eh, what?
Oh, not at all: the chair was old –
Queen Anne, or so we have been told.
We've got at least a dozen more:
Just leave the pieces on the floor.
I want you to admire our view:
Come nearer to the window do;
And look how beautiful . . . Tut, tut!
You didn't see that it was shut?
I hope you are not badly cut!
Not hurt? A fortunate escape!
Amazing! Not a single scrape!
And now, if you have finished tea,
I fancy you might like to see

A little thing or two I've got.
That china plate? Yes, worth a lot:
A beauty too . . . Ah, there it goes!
I trust it didn't hurt your toes?
Your elbow brushed it off the shelf?
Of course: I've done the same myself.
And now, my dear Sir Smashum – Oh,
You surely don't intend to go?
You *must* be off? Well, come again,
So glad you're fond of porcelain.

E.V. Rieu

(Another) Rhymer

I was One
I'd just . . .

I was Two
no longer . . .

Then at Three
I felt like . . .

When I was Four
I'd grown some . . .

At Five
I was fully . . .

Then at Six
I played around with coloured . . .

At Seven
life was . . .

And at Eight
I found a . . .

When I was Nine
the world was . . .

When I was Ten
we built a . . .

But when I was Eleven
I ran out of rhymes.

Matt Simpson

A Song for England

An' a so de rain a-fall
An' a so de snow a-rain

An' a so de fog a-fall
An' a so de sun a-fail

An' a so de seasons mix
An' a so de bag-o'-tricks

But a so me understan'
De misery o' de Englishman.

Andrew Salkey

On Prince Frederick

Here lies Fred,
Who was alive and is dead:
Had it been his father,
I had much rather;
Had it been his brother
Still better than another;
Had it been his sister,
No one would have missed her;
Had it been the whole generation,
So much the better for the nation:
But since 'tis only Fred,
Who was alive and is dead,
There's no more to be said.

Anon

Ozone Friendly Poem

It won't damage the EARTH,
or pollute the sea
it won't psych your mind
neither poison your body
these words have power
when used properly.
Because
This poem is OZONE FRIENDLY.

Words can be creative
words can sound great
we can use words to instruct
and to communicate,
these words are not destructive
violating a tree.
Because
This poem is OZONE FRIENDLY.

My words take shape
they are organised
they won't burn the EARTH'S skin
like pesticides
they're not manufactured using CFCs.
Because
This poem is OZONE FRIENDLY.

Digest these words
feel positive
don't panic, get stressed
they're free from additives,
you won't regurgitate them
like smoke from a factory.
Because
This poem is OZONE FRIENDLY.

These words are SAFE
I can testify
they won't destroy the OZONE LAYER
beyond the sky,
you can analyse this poem
in a laboratory.
You'll find
This poem is OZONE FRIENDLY.

Recycle, regenerate
don't waste energy
conservation of the EARTH
is just a part of the key
and I'll keep on using these words
well naturally.
You see
This poem is OZONE FRIENDLY.

Levi Tafari

I'd Never Fall in Love
With a Girl

I'd never fall in love with a *girl*.

I might fall in love with my new tracksuit top
or my bike
or my mum –
but I'd never fall in love with a *girl*.

I might fall in love with my old casie football
or Liverpool FC
or Auntie Sandra
(she's really nice,
but she's grown up,
and anyway she's married to my Uncle Eddie),
But I'd never fall in love with a *girl*.

I might fall in love with Tessa Jones,
but she's not a girl at all really.
She can run faster,
climb higher, fight harder
and kick a ball further
than any of the boys.

I might *even* fall in love
with my mate Stephen
(if he'd let me, that is) –
except he can't run as fast,
or climb as high, or fight as hard,
or kick a ball as far
as Tessa Jones . . .

But I'd *never* fall in love
WITH A GIRL.

Dave Ward

I Asked the Little Boy
Who Cannot See

I asked the little boy who cannot see,
'And what is colour like?'
'Why, green,' said he,
'Is like the rustle when the wind blows through
The forest; running water, that is blue;
And red is like a trumpet sound; and pink
Is like the smell of roses; and I think
That purple must be like a thunderstorm;
And yellow is like something soft and warm;
And white is a pleasant stillness when you lie
And dream.'

Anon

Acknowledgements

The compiler and publishers wish to thank the following for permission to use copyright material:

John Agard, 'The Older the Violin the Sweeter the Tune' from *Say it Again Granny*, Bodley Head, by permission of Random House UK; **Gerard Benson**, 'Hlep' from *The Magnificent Callisto* by Gerard Benson, Blackie/Puffin, by permission of the author; **James Berry**, 'Okay, Brown Girl, Okay' from *Playing a Dazzler*, Hamish Hamilton. Copyright © James Berry, 1996, by permission of Penguin Books; **Charles Causley**, 'King Foo Foo' from *Collected Poems for Children* by Charles Causley, Macmillan, by permission of David Higham Associates on behalf of the author; **Paul Cookson**, 'Coolscorin'Matchwinnin'Celebratin'Striker', first published in *Elephant Dreams*, Macmillan (1998), and with David Harmer, 'FA Rules OK', first published in *Ere We Go*, ed. David Orme, Macmillan (1993), by permission of the author; **Pie Corbett**, 'Wings', by permission of the author; **John Desmond**, 'Early Start', by permission of the author; **Emily Dickinson**, 'I'm Nobody'[Poem 288] from *The Poems of Emily Dickinson*, ed. Ralph W. Franklin, The Belknap Press of Harvard University Press, Copyright © 1998 by the President and Fellows of Harvard College. Copyright © 1951, 1955, 1979 by the President and Fellows of Harvard College; **Peter Dixon**, 'My Sister's Getting Married' from *Grand Prix* by Peter Dixon, Macmillan, by permission of the author; **Nisha Doshi**, 'A Mouthful of Manhatten' from *Inky Foot* (1996) Young Writers Competition, by permission of W H Smith; **Richard Edwards**, 'Oh Ozzie' from *The House that Caught a Cold*, Viking (1991), by permission of the author; **Max Fatchen**, 'Just in Case' from *Wry Rhymes for Troublesome Times* by Max Fatchen, Kestrel (1983), by permission of John Johnson Ltd on behalf of the author; **Pam Gidney**, 'A Perfect Match' first published in *You'll Never Walk Alone*, ed. David Orme, Macmillan (1995), by permission of the author; **Prabhu Guptara**, 'In praise of noses' first published in *Can I Buy A Slice of Sky?*, ed. Grace Nichols, Blackie (1991), by permission of the author; **David Harmer**, 'Little Lisa', and with Paul Cookson, 'FA Rules OK' first published in *Ere We Go*, ed. David Orme, Macmillan (1993), by permission of the author; **Elizabeth Jennings**, 'The Snake's Warning' from *A Spell of Words*, Macmillan Children's Books, by permission of David Higham Associates on behalf of the author; **Mike Jubb**, 'The Alien Wedding'. Copyright © Mike Jubb, by permission of the author; **Rudyard Kipling**, 'The Way Through the Woods', by permission of A P Watt on behalf of The National Trust for Places of Historic Interest or Natural Beauty; **John Latham**, 'Weasels', by permission of the author; **Dennis Lee**, 'On Tuesdays I Polish My Uncle' from *Alligator Pie*, Macmillan of Canada. Copyright © 1974 by Dennis Lee, by permission of Westwood Creative Artists on behalf of the Author; **Lindsay MacRae**, 'Perfect Paula' and 'Rant About Pants' from *You Canny Shove Yer Granny off a Bus!*, Viking. Copyright © Lindsay MacRae,